The Chances of Harm

ALSO BY ADRIAN RICE

POETRY
Muck Island
Impediments
The Mason's Tongue
Hickory Haiku
The Clock Flower
Hickory Station
The Strange Estate: New & Selected Poems 1986-2017

NONFICTION
The Tin God

AS EDITOR
Signals
Life of the Lough
Sea & Shore
Around the Lough
A Conversation Piece: Poetry and Art
        (edited with Angela Reid)
Lough Views
Exploring the Lough: Creative Activities
    for the Primary School Classroom
        (edited with Molly Freeman)
Insights
Shore Lines

The Chances of Harm

for
Heather –
with love & thanks!

Sláinte!

Poems by

Adrian Rice

Adrian
8/29/24
Hickory x.

Press 53
Winston-Salem

Press 53, LLC
PO Box 30314
Winston-Salem, NC 27130

First Edition

Cover image, "Graveyard Hawk,"
Copyright © 2022 by Molly Rice

Cover design by Micah Rice

Author photograph by Bobbie Hanvey,
Bobbie Hanvey Photographic Archives,
John J. Burns Library, Boston College,
Courtesy of the Trustees of Boston College

Library of Congress Control Number
2024939010

ISBN 978-1-950413-83-6

A Note from the Publisher

Since the author of this book hails from Belfast, Northern Ireland, and this book will be distributed worldwide, the editor has chosen to honor the rules of United Kingdom grammar and punctuation to preserve the voice and spirit of the author and his work. No words have been Americanized by removing the "u" from "colour" or the second "e" in "acknowledgements"; likewise, commas and periods have been left outside the quotation marks, in spite of it irritating the publisher and editor when U.S. authors do this.

Acknowledgements

The author is grateful to the editors of the publications where the following poems first appeared:

Asheville Poetry Review, "The Chances of Harm" & "The Red-Headed Woodpecker"

Crossing The Rift: North Carolina Poets on 9/11 & Its Aftermath, edited by Joseph Bathanti & David Potorti, "US"

Open-Eyed, Full-Throated: An Anthology of American/Irish Poets, edited by Nathalie Anderson, "While I Slept", "Together", & "The Frailty of Man"

The Honest Ulsterman, "The Longley Line"

Vox Populi, "Beginning to Learn"

The author would also like to thank some significant encouragers and helpers along the way: Nathalie Anderson (American Conference for Irish Studies), Joan Barasovska (Flyleaf Books, Chapel Hill), Joseph Bathanti, Gerard Beirne (The Irish Literary Times), Libby Bernardin (Litchfield Tea & Poetry Series), Patrick Bizarro (exemplary critic), Lynda Bouchard (Literary Latte Podcast), Cathy Brown (Seamus Heaney HomePlace, Bellaghy), Jimmy Brown, Star Brown, Erin Hallagan Clare (Story Parlor, Asheville), Jeff Davis & Lockie Hunter (WordPlay Radio), Ian Duhig, Kristie Ennis, Keith Flynn, Beth Frye, Eric Hart, Gareth Higgins (The Porch), Bob Hinkle (White Horse, Black Mountain), Rick Klima, the much-missed Kim Lenaghan (BBC NI), Greg McClure, Scott McKendry, Mel McMahon, Eamonn Mallie ('Covid-19 Poetry'), Jessica Martell, Alan Mearns, Vachel Miller, Chrisanne & Lamar Mitchell, Sheryl Mohn, Peter Nelsen, Bill Nevins (Irish Poetry Salon, New Mexico), Rebekah O'Hara, Micheal O'Siadhail, Lois Palmer, Marty Quinn, Christopher Reid, Matthew Rice, Andrew Roycroft, Leslie M. Rupracht (Waterbean Poetry Night), Carol Rumens, Richard Rankin Russell (Association of Literary Scholars, Critics & Writers), Matthew Ryan Shelton, Michael Simms, Andrew Sneddon, Jie Tan, Dylan Tashjian (Hickory Playground

'Quarantine Diaries' initiative), Woodrow Trathen & Dorothy Maguire, Jeff Vahlbusch, Belinda Walzer, Weymouth Center for the Arts & Humanities, Mary Jane White, and artist, Ross Wilson.

Bumping into my birthday-buddy, Kevin Morgan Watson, in Winston-Salem back in 2012, is all the evidence I need of poetry providence. This is our fourth book together, and I couldn't have found a better home than with Kevin, Chris and the team at Press 53. Big thanks, too, to my poet-son Matt, especially, and to poetry-mates Alan and Scotty for the usual cold eyes on the poems as they appeared. My deepest thanks and love go to my wonderful wife Molly (who this time supplied the—'actual'—hawk pic for the cover image) and to Micah (our whizz-kid who designed the cover). And, as always, much love to my three kids back Home, Matthew, Charis and Charlotte; and to my mother, and brothers.

Contents

Birds are a hope: they can find the islands left.

—William Stafford

At the entrance, my bare feet on the dirt floor,
Here, gusts of heat; at my back, white clouds.
I stare and stare. It seems I was called for this:
To glorify things just because they are.

—Czesław Miłosz

The secret wish of poetry is to stop time.

—Charles Simic

Children playing with knives.
Children swearing. Children
running a country.

—William Stafford

The Frailty of Man

for Malcolm Guite

One night he went sailing tied to a mast in a storm
aged sixty-five, enjoying the frailty of man
The clouds cursed the sea and the sea cursed the clouds all night long
on a date with the dark, flirting with fate until dawn

Fear was a
Fear was a
Fear was a
Fear was a friend

Fear was a
Fear was a
Fear was a
Fear was a friend

Fear was a friend and loneliness gave him her hand
they waltzed through the rain that the wind played like strings in a band
The ship rose and fell as it curdled its way through the foam
he was far from the land but felt he was closer to home

The Chances of Harm

How Do Poems Appear?

for Bill Knott

.

In
visible
ink.

The Chances of Harm

It arrives like God.
Living killing machine.
Silent hearse of the air

rolling in on no wheels.
Makes perfect weight
between wide wings.

Uttermost branch
of the tallest tree.
All judge and jury.

Lord of No Doubt.
I am species-safe.
So, too, the buried bones

of these fields of death
whose headstones are tills
awaiting the cha-ching

of the last trump.
A big daylight owl
seems unimpressed,

blinking the chances of harm.
A cardinal goes off
like a car alarm.

Just Here to Walk

As I embark on my early morning walk,
big American robins move like the great
Franz Beckenbauer across the deserted

YMCA soccer grounds,
advancing in a regimental wave,
taking the empty goalmouths by storm.

Effortlessly, they unstitch the worm ground.
Maybe they're natural descendants of portly
Irish robins, whose dreams of bigness

have been suitably fulfilled. Or maybe not.
Maybe they're just the strange children
of portly wee Irish robins. One never knows.

Either way, I watch them as I circle the track,
trying not to think about them, as such thought
might mean a poem. And sure, I'm just here to walk.

Beginning to Learn

First walk around our Oakwood neighbourhood,
down past the silent school and into the cemetery.
I chose to spend longer in the graveyard to avoid
the living as much as possible. Not in the way
I normally do, to be honest, just to be alone,
but this time to try to stay away from other
walkers who might be out, in case they'd worry

we'd pass by each other too close for Covid
comfort, invading each other's 6-ft zone.
Last time I felt such an unnatural hush
was when all the Irish birdlife suddenly shushed
as the last century turned with a full eclipse.
As I got back close to home I noticed,
for the first time ever, a couple of robins

in the middle of the road outside our house,
pecking away at bits of mossy grass breaking
through the tarmacadam. The robins moved
slowly, unfussed, not their normal edgy selves,
no usual fear of big wheels rolling past.
It's like they know. Already discern.
What we are only slowly beginning to learn.

Mimus Polyglottos

Stock-still in sunshine in the graveyard,
close to a perfectly plump bush,
listening to a northern mockingbird
running the river of its songs
and sounds like it is auditioning
for voicemail salesbird of the year.
Such full-throated impersonation
in a place of silenced mouths.

'Mimus polyglottos', many-tongued
thrush, we have them on the evening
avenue, with a shorter playlist.
In an old graveyard, where humans
are hushed, the bird zone is busy,
so the mockingbird is working hard
in call and chatburst to mark its ground,
even falling for fakery

from me, pursing out my whistle stuff,
chuffed to think it sounds like something
worth imitating. And I wonder
what the other birds make of these
marvellous mimics; if they feel mocked,
resent them as flashy showoffs,
secretly envy their wizardry,
just accept them for what they are.

Or do they pity them as 'Legions'
in their midst, sin-singing out of
their heads like they're biblically possessed?
Whichever, whatever, our thrush
of many-tongues, may you continue
to channel the best of their songs,
spinning harmless mimicry among
those who know your fake message best.

Light That Isn't Moon

This light that isn't moon,
this windless silence,
this being in the empty fullness
of something gathering.

We know it's coming,
been carefully predicted.
Unless the End comes first,
it will surely happen.

Fresh from high country
the night sky's fixing
to pull a big white sheet
over us to keep us

quiet for a little while,
to soften our coughs,
to tuck in our piedmont beds.
Retired already to theirs,

most of my neighbours
will miss the first soft sieve
from Catawba clouds.
I could take Alexa at her word,

I could linger until her 3 a.m.
to see those first flakes fall,
but I'll choose to sleep instead,
asking her to flick off lights

to save for the morning
with my wife and child
the timeless surprise of snow.
We wake in our first home

to world as immaculate duvet,
snow-sabbath the roads and driveways,
fences a sequence of frosted crosses,
each house deliciously iced.

Of the Dead or Dying

On a slip road off
Lenoir-Rhyne Boulevard
three huge buzzards open
and close their capes
frocking to and fro,

then step out and back,
instinctively observing
the Green Cross Code.
Call the one in front
the leader, the bravest, the hungriest,

though not the most foolish.
He's so humanly wary
of the rush hour road.
Still, he's risking all
for the sake of a roadkill

so big and fresh the cars
swerve to avoid it;
a roadkill like a fleshly
riveting Chaim Soutine.
I hurry on, driving

my son to his reading test.
Where did they come from?
How so quick to arrive?
Nothing ever goes unseen.
Something is always watching.

The Homeless Man Walked in the Graveyard

The homeless man walked in the graveyard,
backpacked, floppy hat, unlit cigarette,
eyeing the richly wreathed grave now shaded
beneath the Bass-Smith cemetery tent.
Whatever family had gathered to mourn
had retreated to their cars and gone home.
Rain broth was brewing; he could smell it.
When it started to spit, he took a slow
way around to the deserted gravesite.
With his backpack as a makeshift pillow,
he stretched himself out on the grassy ground
beside the fresh mound, and lit the cigarette.
Inhaling/exhaling thanks for cover,
he lay there until the worst was over.

The Plastic Cross

Close to the scene
of a big tree down,
seemingly carriaged
mid-air—
a train falling off
a dead-end bridge,
uncoupling on the ground—
the young red fox caught
both their eyes
and held them.
The dog stopped
and looked around,
looking for whatever
they were following.
The young red fox
doggied on,
stopping to look back
once or twice
before brushing
through a hedge.
The dog pulled
on the lead and the lead
toppled a plastic cross
planted beside a grave,
which she tried to
replace in the gravesoil.
When he tried to move it
to a skinny flower pot
to straighten it
to make it look better,
it lifted up in one piece
then fell from his hands
in three pieces.

They jigsawed the cross
back in place.
What can you make
of a cross falling apart
in your hands?

Even Summer

Watching the hired hands
in our neighbour's yard
circling like busy border collies,
herding the leaves with leaf blowers
into a kerbside bank of brittle gold.
Even summer must get old.

These Are the Days

It is *some* evening,
sunshine still
in the tips
of the slightly
staggering trees,
and I want to nip
over the road
to the lanky teen
shooting slick hoops
in his grandmother's
backyard while she
happily rakes round
shrubs, tidying up
her careful gardening,
and whisper in his ear.
And when he turns to me
with a look of—Yeah,
I know, I know—
I will say it again,
and again, and again
until he goes beyond being
close to getting it.

US

The professor pulls
the screen down,
and projects a map
of the world onto it.

As you all know,
we have been at war
in several countries
for many years now.
Not to embarrass anyone,
but can anyone point
to those countries
on the map?

No one can.

OK, the professor says, *ok.*
And then—

Well, here's the thing—
most of those who
we're at war with,
when asked to point
to US, can.

Craven

What's a dollar worth
to one who craves a billion?

What's a country worth
to one who craves to rule?

What's another's life worth
to one who craves his own?

Capitol

What do you want with me?
Democracy?
In God's name don't torture me!

What is your name?

My name is Legion,
for we are many.
I beg you, do not send
us away from the Capitol.
Send us among the Party,
let us go into them.

So they went into the Party.

Then a wave was made manifest
that took them to the sea.

The Red-Headed Woodpecker

When the red-headed woodpecker who appears
each afternoon outside our bedroom window
tailor-fitted in his red white and blackness

fidgeting up and down the trunk sap-sucking
tears my eyes away from off the breaking news
I can't help but think that he is mimicking

a person banging their head against a wall
And in that dear Lord oh can't you hear America
singing he most surely represents us all

Too Close to Home

Fuck the NRA!

What did you say?

Fuck the NRA!

His side-taking surprised me.
I'd pegged him for a pistol boy.

You heard me right the first time,
didn't ya?
Listen now—
who runs the NRA,
and where do they live?

I've no idea. Why?

Come on now, son,
from where you come from
you should know.
And you should know—

the only way they're ever
goin' to change their tune
is when the bullets get
too close to home.

Of All Nights

in memory of C. K. Williams

Of all nights, I couldn't
help but notice

how when the little
citronella candle tea light

was brimming with wax,
it was easily put out

by the slightest breeze.
But when it was

almost on empty
it was burning bright,

because its very
life depended on it.

Forever

for Sydney on her thirtieth

Goodness, Sydney!
Did you hear it?
Just now,

the little wren's sudden song
from the dead bough of a tree
fairly warbled the air:

Remember!
As long as you're alive,
O lucky girl,
You have forever!

Villa

for Timothy Wayne Freeman

There are no unsacred places;
there are only sacred places,
and desecrated places.
    —Wendell Berry

You don't hear it on quietish weekends when you arrive,
but there's always someone building nearby in Florida,
the land never being allowed to simply rest and breathe,
to just *be* under the sun. There's always the weekday
drone and clatter of a digger gulping its fill, chomp
after chomp, waterfalls of earth and its stones
building into mounds of dirtstack after dirtstack,
like someone sinking a metal scooper into
an arcade of coins, scooping them up and dumping
them into big piles to carry away. And always,
about as poorly-rich as bank tellers, hired hands
do most of the work while making the least of the money.
Such desecration makes the canal-side villa, with pool,
that we rent to make memories, on the summery run
from our Covid routines, grabbing for the child a slice
of the privilege-pie that, as children, escaped us.

For Them

A fear of dying
maybe best
belongs to the most
truly alive; to those
who are most aware;
who love living.

They're not less brave,
perhaps, or less faith-
full, but have the most
to lose—
their truly loved ones;
this life;

themselves.

The Other Day

The other day
they held a hug
and shortened
the old oval table—

sure it made such
rounded sense
now that their last
was college able.

Heresy

Unless we
can see it,
it doesn't
exist.

Science
has put that
heresy
to rest.

Prayer

How good to free
a butterfly—

caught in a loose
porch web—

opening and
closing itself

like hands
perpetually

in prayer.

The Moneymakers

It is easier for a camel to go through the eye of a needle,
than for a rich man to enter into the kingdom of God.
—Matthew 19:24

I deigned to suffer two blazing
American moneymakers tonight,
and my spiritual blood was boiling.

Apparently, we will always—
misquoting Jesus—have the filthy rich
and the pathetic poor with us,

and that's perfectly OK, apparently,
as long as we have our wealthy middle class,
suitably, and proportionately, healthy.

I told them that we are what we read,
and that I sensed that they weren't well-read,
though they were certainly more than well-heeled.

They proffered the stereotypical tirade
against the native foreigner; the drunken Irish.
O men, as you lay your tipsy heads down in bed,

I'll be writing a little poem about you, I said.

Philosophy

It's your turn, daddy,
to burst the bubbles.

It's ok, son.
I don't like to burst them.
I prefer to watch them.

Are you sad that they
just go away?

Yes, son, I am.

It is sad that they can't stay.

I know, son.

But we can blow more
bubbles another day.

Already Happened

Some people settle down to write their wills.
Not having much that's worldly-worthy
I haven't yet been bothered to comply.
I worry, though, which loved ones or places
I may, or may not, get to see again,
so I dreamplan to give my time to them
before the inevitable arrives;
before those unpredictable goodbyes.

Meantime, I feel someone sympathetically
watching, who understands how we regret
sometimes living terribly unwisely;
who knows very well what we know and then forget,
that one more meeting may never happen;
last leavings having already happened.

Only Our Clothes

Only our clothes seem to keep us basically happy,
as fundamentally happy as we can be,
given the circumstances of each ordinary moment.

O I know well what we say—but seriously,
why we ever had to evolve with the need
for clothing is surely still mysterious, especially

for the naturally promiscuous. What kind of evolutionary
cock-up was at work? I'm well tempted to believe
that we were all once happily naked,

until something terrible happened to make us shy.
Otherwise, why? Deep down, we all know that clothes
are fake. A cover up. A necessity born of some mistake.

The dominantly evolved being the most naked
certainly makes no earthly sense. The fish, the bear,
the monkey, the bird, need no extra clothing,

just their feathers, skin and sheen. Did we give up the sea
for temporal hairiness, an undesirable hairiness,
just to be clothed, after all, in the skin of others?

And what is it that we're covering up?
To sit about naked—why so unnatural, so gross?
And when we don't, what exactly have we lost?

Most of us even insist on entering the grave in full regalia.
Still, many of the living are hot advocates of skimping—
maybe the initial need for covering, then the shedding,

is just an evolutionary circle arcing back to a Garden idyll.

Big Deal

Sure the best that we have done
is to merely mimic everything
under the sun, improving
on nothing natural, which is our way
of saying that this is what it is—
what is *is*—and what once was,
and ever has been, evermore shall be.

Big deal. Who cares? So what? Let's shop!

Even the strip lighting under
the polished bar in Asheville's Lab
is copy-coloured to fancy-up
those denimed thighs or shaven legs.
And we know that this is all for show,
all man-mastered show, and that it's
all so-so. Whatever we do is already done.

Big deal. Who cares? So what? Let's shop!

It's all so much of an old imitation.
Strung along the bar are solid,
breathing human beings, and all the flash
and flicker of human invention
is still so far short of this real.
Yes, we all know, in the end,
that we've managed much that's all just show.

Big deal. Who cares? So what? Let's shop!

And who cares about tomorrow?
It's just a sunlit or cloudy sorrow,
a repetition of all sorts, senses
of wonder run down to routine boredoms.
When there was just one galaxy, we were
enthralled. Now that there's billions—
So what? Big deal. Now that there are

Big deal. Who cares? So what? Let's shop!

more than plenty, *who cares? Let's shop!*
Boredom. All is boredom. There's nothing
new under the burning wo-man-known sun.
Even the stars' alignments lack excitement
along the studded pelt above the mountain road.
And sure some of them are already dead,
taking their sweet eons of time to tell us.

Big deal. Who cares? So what? Let's shop!

So many worlds out there! So many worlds!
So what? Let's shop! What does it prove?
What would it deny? When the distance between
people is more than what can be described ...
But Orion's Belt! The Seven Sisters! The Plough!
Ah, even the diamonds of The Milky Way, star-stones,
only really shine when we're mopily alone.

Big deal. Who cares? So what? Let's shop!

Until we drop.

Money-Falls

My study bookshelves
are a money-falls arcade,
so much loose change banked

up and ready for the drop,
just waiting for the nudge
of another neglected coin.

My little son loves to strew
those that fall around the house,
scattering them like seeds,

hard seeds that don't grow.
So we're forced to use them
like tiny stepping stones,

until we get tired enough
to round them up again,
and put them back upon

the high shelves. There they
sit with other pocket-less
memorabilia, like Tums,

and toothpicks, or a coated
aspirin, waiting for their
penny-pinching time to shine.

Times

Supermoon's risen
at the end of our street.

It wouldn't surprise me
if it suddenly dropped

out of the sky.
For given the times,

what could surprise
you or I?

This Letting Go

Why wouldn't we invest
them with such significance?
This letting go of leaves
from the avenue trees
which feels like the deaths
of so many people,
each struggling to hang on

until the very last breath;
all of them subject
to each sudden
mood swing
of wind that sends
showers of them
wending to the ground
every time it lifts.

But we come and go,
they seem to say,
we come and go,
and at least we're not alone
like so many of you—
just look at us lushing
the dainty driveways

with our leafy selves!
And if we hadn't have fallen,
how long, in this world,
in your world,
do you think we could've
happily hung on?
How long?

The Night Trees

The night trees
stand still
in their quietnesses

only raising
their voices
when the invisible—

travelling from
somewhere

to somewhere—

shivers them
into soughs

Risk

Seems they're never bored
with their constant scooting

about the trees, rubbing
their beaks on branches,

their heads and tails
casual counterweights

to keep them centred,
so that telegraph lines

are no more than welcome
walk-wires in the air,

easy to negotiate,
with no net needed.

Maybe boredom just
doesn't enter into it;

they do what they do
and are happily done with it.

But I suspect they're
natural adrenalin junkies,

much more alert than us,
knowing better than us

that at any sunny moment
everything's at risk.

Alone and Always

for Wystan

They were never alone
and always too busy,
equipped to ignore
what they knew to be true.

In a bombarded world,
massed with imagery,
they steered their screen
ships into the blue.

A Strange Surprise

Morning clouds graze on the football field,
their foggy sides in our faces.
I'm alone, following two dogs being led

by their owner around the walking track,
one a golden brown, one a pearly white.
The older dog, head down, pads slowly

in a straight line, middle of the path;
the other, younger, bigger, wanders in and out
of the dewy field, straining the leash,

wanting to play, sniffing everything in its way.
I watch it leave a trail of paw prints behind
on the bone-dry path, like perfectly draped

damp half-circle doggy valances. As I
come back around the walking track I draw
alongside two elderly women wondering

how the doggy valances came to be. So—
what are the chances?—I stop to tell them the story
of what I saw. I say, *Two dogs were walking here,*

one cutting in and out of the football field,
the other not, so only one of them left a trace.
One smiles, and turns, and says,

This reminds me of that 'Footprints' poem
that people share, the 'Anon' one, you know,
about Jesus carrying us while we are unaware?

I must tell my husband when I get home,
he really loves that 'Footprints' poem. I nod,
and smile, and rush to walk on, when she says,

You sure there were two dogs, and not just one?
her doubting, a strange surprise.
I saw them, I say. *Two of them. With my own eyes.*

High-Rise

The family have left me
for our new bed,
the plush plinth
of a Stearns & Foster,
a high-rise miracle
of polyurethane foam,
blended rayon and polyester,
with fibre batting,
soft silk and wool,
and firm innerspring features.

They have fallen
for its moulding charms,
drugged by their sudden
exposure to comfort,
accepted as a cloud-thick
favour from above.
It is their quiet island
of rest from the day,
a strand of foam and feather,
a newfound America.

Alive

One of those words
that is always in danger of dying
will have to do,
if it's not, in some circles,
already dead.
And let's even add a weary
exclamation point—*Wow!*

Porched, reading Simic's latest,
The Lunatic, I look up
to see a first firefly—nature's renewable
energy—flame from left
to right across the neighbour's yard.

Just one, has to be just one,
moving along at even height
in what seems like a plum line,
going on and off in rhythmic time,
like lifeless bleeps on a heart monitor ....
when—*Wow!*—one bright jump higher.

The Silent Space

Given a choice by the gentleman, my third-grader son
elected to have me join him in the soundproofed room
to take his hearing test. Shy-seeming to the audiologist,
his mother and I knew him better than that,
how he wasn't truly shy so much as unimpressed
with common ceremony. We were wholeheartedly
wrong, it appeared, for since he had hardly
heard much in one ear for all of his young life
he'd been innocently distanced by such loss,
sending anti-social signals he wasn't guilty of.

I sat behind him in the vaulty booth, sworn to quiet,
kindly ordered to keep really still: just there for him in
silent support, pretending to be parentally composed.
I couldn't hear the doctor's words when he began the test
from behind the cloudy one-way mirror that hid his face,
the inter-booth exchange between their headphoned selves,
for my boy to listen to and show that he had caught
the words the doctor threw. He sat there motionless,
concentrated, as grown up as he always was when faced
with the new that those much older would struggle with.

I couldn't hear the words, only he could seek their sound,
but knew when they were found by how he'd physically
respond, raising his hand casually like a cattle bidder
when a word came through, or thumbing a button
when a word barge docked, not sank, along his ear canal.
Sometimes he spoke in answer to the mystery words,
sending back those he'd been asked to repeat: some wrong
no doubt, like errant echoes, some like perfect rhymes,
but all were simple words now solemnly renewed,
words and phrases rinsed of the ordinariness of daily use

in the inner sanctum hush of that listening room:
words like *house, home, sailboat, mother, laughter,*
and *sunshine, doctor, flavour, good, past,* and *before.*
Ice-cream, I remember, raised and left a ripple of a smile
and a sneaky lifting of his eyes to meet with mine.
I felt involved but helpless, hovering in that room,
unable to lend him my ears, though given age I'm
unsure whether mine would catch the words' drift better.
Which reminded me of sitting in a virtual online room
with my Irish son, listening to the story of his latest poem,

to another tale of sailing solo into the silent space
to bring back messages from behind the vaulted veil;
and how I always will him on to have the ears to find them:
just sitting with him, listening in, only seeing how it's going
by those words he stitches into each carefully crafted verse;
for as he now knows, words that make poems are inaudible
to anyone except those chosen to receive their cargoed charge.
Test was over. Conductive hearing issues, the spoken diagnosis.
We headed home with lollipops and stickers to tell his mother.
Listening well to her, our son's now learning how to live with loss.

The Longley Line

for Michael Longley

Preparing for bed, I rake the grate,
pat the white-hot ashes delicately
with a small black shovel
to keep them tight and intact
and set off for the back door determined
the carpet will remain singe-free.

Not a man on a risky ropewalk,
nor a teenager tiptoeing a lover's landing,
I walk hot ashes into the wind-fresh lane
like Longley walks words along the Longley line.

You

*... because you get everything back, and by everything,
I mean you.*
                    —Jason Schneiderman

It can happen when you're sitting down reading
a poem from the latest Review a poem that you
were going to turn the page on because it looked
like a big clump of words with little hope of being
whatever poetry might be but you get sucked into reading
it nevertheless because you've given it a two line audition—
*The afterlife is an infinity of custom shelving, where everything /
you have ever loved has a perfect place—*
and so you realise with live joy that it's actually
an immediately memorable poem despite its attempts
not to be a poem by design and so despite any flaws
that might surface as you continue to read through it
you start to think all sorts of serious thoughts
inspired by the early contents of the poem and you start
to think that some of the thoughts might actually be
the starting point for one of your own poems
and it's at that minute the phone goes off which is in an
adjoining room and in a split-second decision you rise up off
the toilet with definite speed and you shuffle
from room to room like a proper Chaplin to answer the call
and you miss it just miss it and you stand there phone in hand
checking caller ID knowing how ridiculous you look.

Beginnings

for Raymond Carver

She was thinking, again,
about just how much the dust
on the venetian blind
was annoying her,
just how tired she was,
all done out with pain,
when she heard him come in.

He threw the beer bottles
out by the scruff of their necks,
saw cars surfing on shadows
under a demilune moon,
found himself standing,
nude, in his closet, hanging
clothes on a wooden line.

I Never Dreamed of Any Enormity

The smallest black airborne thing
that settled on my newfangled *Walden*,
performing all kinds of miraculously
multi-wing maneuvers
and full body curls
under the microscope
of my latest reading lenses,
right opposite the passage beginning,
"I never dreamed of any enormity
greater than I have consulted.
I never knew, and never shall know,
a worse man than myself",
only took the length of itself—
the time it took me to pencil-trace
the interchange—before I looked up
to see that it had vanished.

Self-Assembly

for John Hewitt

On hands and knees,
assembling cheap
shelving to take
the book weight.

Still stacking
the wooden tombs.

More flat pack gaffer
than apprentice.

A liver spot or two.

More coffin-maker
than crib-man.

These shelves believe
in resurrection,
imagination breathing
through dead sheaves.

New light dawning
with every read page.

Yard Work

The neighbour and I.
We joke across the avenue aisle
about the onset of porch time.
While praising the advent
of all that it means, we
comradely lament the yard work
that has to be tholed.

As if we are somehow
equals in the seasonable labour.
As if I could shake a spade
at her miraculous endeavours,
her skilled green-fingered-ness
her laudable efforts to keep
her garden, and shrubbery, pristine.

It's almost as if we are fellow poets,
fast farmers of verses.
As if one of us isn't slacking
in what it takes to carry
the living thing forward,
not lacking in showing
the proper respect

for the copious rose,
the sculpted shrub,
the blade of grass,
the whole blooming lot.
As if one of us isn't lazily inattentive,
undeserving of the true line
that is the all of spring.

Protagonist

I felt the desk move
when the big tree fell,
though what had fallen
was a mystery then.
One of my neighbours'
favourites, one of mine,
protagonist of many
a porch-sit poem.
The thud that shook my room
was the main trunk
coming down,
laid out now
like the family head.
Branches alongside
like children dead.
A truck arrived
like a timely hearse.
The neighbours were
close to tears.
I have to say,
I'll miss its oceanic presence,
its wavy greenness,
how storms made
shingles of its leaves.
How it let the sky through
in lakes and loughs
of watery light.
That night,
I dreamed that
as it crashed
it washed us all away.

Trapeze

Two hungry birds—
the one bird?—

catching bugs in
glorious mid-air,

hammocking
back and forth

between two
dusky trees,

flight paths slung
like the perfect arcs

of trapeze artists
or the tight-lipped

smileys of darkness.

Gone

The neighbours
have gone.

No one knows
for how long.

Their house sits
at its own

front door
waiting for them

to come home.

Rescued

in memory of Kim Lenaghan

The day you went,
after the cloudy scrawl,
the sun laid

its bright blanket
on the lawns
that we passed

on our evening stroll,
walking our rescue
to the graveyard.

Scrolling through
your page I'm not
surprised to see

you rescued three.
And often
the likes of me.

Fell

The young bird landed
the old branch broke

The branch fell
they both fell

The one down
the other up

Dark Confidence

A first: two young ravens
command the garden,

their calls like two
quick coughs, then

two squeaky gates.
Black-cloaked and slick,

they've arrived like two
Olde English Sheriffs

looking to collect some rent.
I admire their dark confidence,

but my money's on our local robins,
whose humble homes are Shire-sent.

Circus

Innocently thinking that life
is like a circus alright,
when a young girl on a tricycle

appears from behind the hedge
at a surprising rate of knots
followed by her bearded father

holding the middle of the road,
in green top and yellow shorts,
riding, I kid you not, a unicycle,

his arms searching for balance,
his torso twisting, knees criss-
crossing like he needs to pee,

followed by another bearded man
fast-walking himself into view
from behind the same hedge

pursued by his young daughter,
both of them being pulled along
by big dogs at the end of long leads,

like they're both driving sledges
across some arctic waste,
and squirrels are running the wires,

trapezing through the trees,
and robins are pulling
worms out of the ground,

juggling them in their beaks,
and as I holler for Molly and Micah
to quickly come see,

sat waiting for them to appear,
I reach for the lukewarm
table-topped bottle to check

it is non-alcoholic beer.

Idles

A young man pulls
up in his father's car,
swerves the driveway.

Idles for a few seconds.
A young woman skips
from the side door

of her mother's house
into the passenger seat.
Lustlit with loveliness.

They quickly kiss.
He puts his hand
gently on the back

of her headrest,
reverses, takes off.
Blossoming trees,

length of the street,
froufrou their skirts
in the bowing breeze.

Together

I love those nippy cardinals
and their feisty wives,

those lipstick-coloured fusiliers,
flitting through blossomed branches

like children through fields of flowers;
fighting back against big bossy robins

who throw their red-coated
weight around the evening garden.

All glory to the clothed-in-feather!
At least they've learned to live together.

Furnace

Against the timely flares
of evening's fireflies,

and the exquisite attentiveness
of each garden bird,

two cell-scabbed youths are
shaking a crossroads STOP sign,

and a middle-aged neighbour
is driving past on the wrong

side of the road, studying their
hand-held device as they go,

their salooned conveyance
like a costly coffin destined

for an invisible furnace.

So I Shook

Someday, then, we will choose differently.
And it will, we believe, make all the difference.
—David Orr

I lifted my eyes
from Orr's book on
"The Road Not Taken"
to see a nimble bug
negotiating the tiled mosaic
of the porch floor,
heading towards me, confidently.

So I shook its world
with a solid foot stamp,
sending it back
the way it came,
back towards the flaming
May-Pole of the glassed
candle it deftly circled,

slipping away and down
into the crack
at the porch's edge.
Next time it tries it on,
I wonder whether its path
will be the same.
Anyway, now the moon's

popped up like a buoy
from the depths
on the ocean of night
without any discernible noise.
And, to the best
of our knowledge,
without any choice.

Cheap Cuts

Sitting in our old Dodge caravan at Walmart,
guarding our wee trooper asleep in the back
worn out from sitting in on mummy's rehearsals,
I was watching the toing and froing
of the walking wounded,
many of them aimed at the pharmacy,
towards the long lines waiting on legal drugs—
the pillbillies, as some people like to call them—
wondering what their lives were like,
what had brought them all the way to this day.

I have been picturing everyone lately
as children, our best childhood selves,
which is enough to break anyone's heart,
for look at how so many of us
little children have managed to turn out.

And I was watching the birds flitting about the car park
using what little trees are in these lots,
thinking—are these birds the working class
versions of the birds from my leafy avenue?
If so, what short birdie straws did they draw?
Did they not graduate from aviary high school?
Would they be full-fledged followers of a feathery Trump?
Would our avenue bird life not want to be seen dead
pecking around with them in a Walmart lot?

So when my mill hill wife returned to the car,
I shared my thoughts, and she bet that there's
more food for them round such lots,
and I thought, yes, maybe more quantity, sure,

but what about quality? Is it more like birdy junk food?
What if we tested their birdy blood for cholesterol levels?

Our avenue birds dine on fat worms and finer crumbs,
crumbled for them deliberately by human hands;
jousting gently with squirrels over provided feeders,
some of them are living in little hand-painted houses.

Vertigo

In an effort to stay grounded, I start each day
with the live download from NASA TV,
my elevenses with the International Space Station.
And I love it when we're treated to a shot from
a camera on an outside limb as the station
hurtles round the earth at 17,500 miles per hour.
Always a spiritual view of earth from up there—

the rim of our blue rock against the alien black ...
But what's important, here, is that little tremor I think
I spot, sometimes, to the body of the techno ship,
as if it's wobbling a bit as it does its speedy lap:
not around the world in eighty days, that's
easy, but between fifteen and sixteen times a day—
surreal sunrise to sunset, a ninety-minute play!

Or maybe I'm imagining it, the tremor,
the wobble, the shudder, but it seems to be there.
And then sometimes when I'm lying down, before dreaming,
or sitting quietly on the porch, reading, writing,
I swear that I can feel the same slight rocking,
and not from the strumming of my own blood
racing round me, like water through the heart of wood,

and not through any human vertigo—I know
a bit about that—but maybe from a universal vertigo,
a deep space sea-swell, an actual axis-shiver,
part of the precarious, gravity-grateful nature
of our earthly lives, as we ourselves revolve and hurtle
on the good ship Earth (the only planet-ark
we know of, for sure) through space at perfect

speed, rippling the cosmic cloth around the slam-dunk
of the sun. Maybe we're never as grounded as we think.

The Waiting Room

My friend is in
that halfway house

between what's
left here

and what might
be waiting there.

It's all that I can do
to share.

Pity Party

Poetical feelings
of 'poor me'—
now there's an affectation

to make one blush.
Poverty is having nothing
in the teeth

of the unforgiving.
The truly poor
have no such

arenas for rapture.
So catch ourselves
on the next time

lacking literary recognition
or understanding
is felt fit

for selfish serenade.
It's really good that somewhere
someone rained on our parade.

"Ulsta"

Sat sipping
creamy pints
with my eldest
on the seafront
of Newcastle,
County Down,
when a couple
of buffed men
stride past,
both of them
pulled along
by big
brown dogs
holding in their
slabbery
mouths
huge
doggy-toy
cheetahs.

Simple

The shadow of the mountainous cloud
must mimic the face of the mountain;

simple, the laws of interrelation
that rule things astral and solid.

That Moment When

they saw the hands

of one claiming
to be the one

upset the tables
they had set up

in his Father's house.

Tables like the ones
those same hands

had no doubt helped
to make back home

in his father's house.

The Starry Messenger

Rocking-chaired
outside The Fat Pelican,
scanning Keithley on
Galileo Galilei—

'The Starry Messenger'—
the old truths
resurfaced once more:
that everything we

ever do or think
is crucially curved,
no matter how straight
it sometimes seems.

O Lost Children
of the Circumference!
O Spokesfolk
of the Eternal Circle!

Pentecost

What to make of the silent pentecost
that doesn't shake a single leaf
left in the overhanging trees

or lift a single hair on the head
but suddenly shoos and shifts
the fallen flakes of autumn

sending them skittering away
a murmuration of leaves
uncloaking the path before us

with the dog and I both stopping
to turn our heads and test the air
looking for God-knows-what

Shard

Sometimes the wrong word
can be closer to truth.
Like the word 'shard',

as in 'showered',
that two-syllable word
alien to my mouth

unless strung as one syllable
by my Belfast tongue—
's h a r d'.

For everywhere I walked
this morning I was
showered with leaves,

even stopping under
one trembling maple
to yell, *Such yellowness!*

And then:
Shard!
Well shard, I tell ye!

Only the dog was there
to be suddenly scared
by the Belfastspeak,

then he, too, happily
stood under the maple
paw-deep in leaf-lets,

tree-shards,
airy adjuncts to branches,
clocking off in droves,

messaging winter.

While I Slept

I was the wick
Unlit at first
As all around me
My birth house
Reassembled itself
From the ground up
Like wax un-melting

Ten or so
The memorable age
Each room reappeared
Each stick of furniture
Showing me what
Had been forgotten
Each family member
Was there

Those now gone
Those still here
And I moved among them
Solid but unseen
I was the wick
Unlit at first
But when everything

Was fully formed
Memory peaked
And I became flame
The house and they
Began to melt away
All that memory
Had rebuilt
While I slept

Mummy

Unwinding the mummy
of the paper towels
reminds me of my own,

who wiped away
our childhood troubles
with no word of a moan,

and managed to pay
all the necessary bills
to keep us a home.

30 Doagh Road

She's my grandmother, or she may be yours,
sitting in her small living room by a real fire,
sanctifying her evening corner of the fireplace.
In shot is the old black-and-white TV
standing stalk on thin brassy legs,

as much a part of the family as anyone else.
In her aproned lap she holds her knitting.
She grows colourful garments from a ball of yarn,
her hands kiting above unspooling wool-skeins.
Those busy needles of ancestral love

are clicking with effortless expertise
while she stages a smile for the camera.
Over the tiled mantelpiece, such as it is,
a family of ducks are forever in flight,
rising towards the moon of a plain white clock,

cheap kind you'd see in local schoolrooms.
The chimney breast is lavishly papered,
dressed up in a floral flourish, unlike
the workaday plainness of the other walls.
On the mantelpiece there's Scottie dog delph,

grandchildren's gift-knacks, small-framed pics,
another clock, a fancy one, polished and centred,
shaped like the Cavehill overlooking the house.
It tells the time, again, time that she is
religiously the last person to idly ignore.

O photographic proof of an old-fashioned
faith in the possibility of family!
O stitcher of seconds of unwasted time
into useful coverings to clothe the given clan!
Take these thanks for your example to that boy; this man.

Airman

in memory of my uncle, John Marks (who loved to 'fly' cars)

All the literati keep
An imaginary friend.
　　　　　—W. H. Auden

Almost sleeping in the bathtub, looking out the window
at the blue sky with a high plane and perfect contrail,
remembering my grandparents' home on the Doagh Road,
Newtownabbey, one sunny afternoon after school,
remembering thinking then that though I'd seen the selfsame
thing many times before, it was a memorable moment,
gazing at the shiny metal glint of the plane's underbelly in the
sun, a thing so high, so small to the eye, soundlessly making
its chalky way through the deep blue sky, moving silently
and fastly slow, slow enough for thought; and now seen again,
today, on a day when I've been feeling, again,
that all of our days have really been just the selfsame day,
and so the anonymous airman of today's sky
is suddenly the same pilot, and I'm the same boy,
and he's been flying for some fifty years across the blue,
now looking down on a man looking up at him
through a bathroom window in Hickory, North Carolina,
gazing up at him and his shiny plane perfectly contrailing
the embersmoke of wonder across his eyes.

Adrian Rice is from Northern Ireland, and has managed to establish himself as a poet on both sides of the Atlantic. He graduated from the University of Ulster with a BA in English & Politics, and an MPhil in Anglo-Irish Literature, and holds an EdD from Appalachian State University (his doctoral dissertation being—Between 'The Planter & The Gael': A Cross-Community Education in Poetry). His first sequence of poems appeared in *Muck Island* (1990), a collaboration with leading Ulster artist, Ross Wilson. Copies of this limited-edition box-set are housed in the The Tate Gallery and The Boston Museum of Fine Arts. In 1997, Rice received the Sir James Kilfedder Memorial Bursary for Emerging Artists. In autumn 1999, as recipient of the US/Ireland Exchange Bursary, he was Poet-in-Residence at Lenoir-Rhyne College, Hickory, North Carolina. His first full poetry collection—*The Mason's Tongue* (1999)—was shortlisted for the Christopher Ewart-Biggs Memorial Literary Prize, nominated for the Irish Times Prize for Poetry, and translated into Hungarian by Thomas Kabdebo (*A Komuves Nyelve*, 2005). In 2002, he co-edited a major Irish anthology entitled, *A Conversation Piece: Poetry and Art* (The Ulster Museum in association with Abbey Press). His poems and reviews have been broadcast internationally on radio and television, and have been published in several international magazines and journals. He has lectured, and given poetry readings, at several conferences, and published articles and book chapters on Irish literature. Selections of his poetry and prose have appeared in both *The Belfast Anthology* and *The Ulster Anthology* (Blackstaff Press, 1999 & 2006) and in *Magnetic North: The Emerging Poets* (Lagan Press, 2006). A chapbook, *Hickory*

Haiku, was published in 2010 by Finishing Line Press, Kentucky. Rice returned to Lenoir-Rhyne College as Visiting Writer-in-Residence for 2005. Since then, Adrian and his wife Molly, and youngest son, Micah, have settled in Hickory. Adrian has taught English and Creative Writing at several local college. Accepting a full-time position at Appalachian State University in 2020, he is now Senior Lecturer. In 2020, he also received the Rennie W. Brantz Award for Outstanding Teaching in the First Year Seminar. Adrian's passion is centered on proving the educational, sustaining power of Poetry and the Arts in his Appalachian classrooms. He has also teamed up with Hickory-based and fellow Belfastman, musician/songwriter Alan Mearns, to form 'The Belfast Boys', a dynamic Irish Traditional Music duo. Their album, *Songs For Crying Out Loud*, regularly airs across the Carolinas. Recent poetry titles, *The Clock Flower* (2013), *Hickory Station* (2015), and *The Strange Estate: New & Selected Poems 1986-2017*, are all published by Press 53. *Hickory Station* was nominated for the Roanoke-Chowan Award for Poetry, and a poem from *Hickory Station*, "Breath", was a Pushcart Prize nominee, and a (London) *Guardian* 'Poem of the Week'. Adrian's poems are also included in Arlen House/Syracuse University Press's, *Open-Eyed, Full-Throated: An Anthology of American/Irish Poets* (2019), and in *Crossing the Rift: North Carolina Poets on 9/11 & Its Aftermath* (Press 53, 2021).

Printed in the USA
CPSIA information can be obtained
at www.ICGtesting.com
LVHW041135140824
788182LV00004B/29